·PARRAGON·

BUILD YOUR OWN
STEAM LOCOMOTIVES

D0333217

Model engineering and artwork by Graham Osborne
Text by Karen Farrington and Nick Constable

THE FIRST TRAINS

Man invented the wheel back in the mists of time and has known about its worth in transporting heavy objects for centuries. And some 450 years ago, the first wheel tracks were invented in the mines of Europe. Wagons laden with heavy loads either shoved by men or pulled by horses moved relentlessly along the rails instead of sinking into the ground. It wasn't until the end of the 18th century, however, that a dream of a machine which moved along under its own power with the help of both wheels and tracks was poised to become a reality.

STEAM LOCOMOTIVES

Steam trains are a thrilling spectacle. Back in the days when they were used every day, children and enthusiastic adults rushed to the railways to wave and cheer when they passed. The smoke pumped from their funnels was a glorious sight.

They are rare sights today, with cleaner, faster trains taking their place on the railways, powered by diesel and electricity. But for many the magic of a steam-powered locomotive will never be forgotten.

Static steam engines had been designed and improved in the 18th century. Determined engineers were kept busy drawing up ideas on how it could be modified to move along. The first working steam locomotive was built by Richard Trevithick in 1804 and sped along with its cargo of

One of the 'modern' steam engines, of the 18th century. They ran on a track size of 1.43 m (4 ft 8½ in), the same as mine tracks.

iron and passengers for nine miles at a speed of 8 km (5 miles) per hour on an ironworks railway in South Wales. The 70 men on the trip were crammed into bumpy wooden carriages designed for coal. But the event was so momentous that none of them gave a second thought to the discomfort and dirt.

The first public railway to use a steam engine was the Stockton and Darlington Railway in 1825. At the controls of the *Locomotion* steam engine was George Stephenson, pioneer of British railways. He towed the owner's coach, 11 coal wagons, a wagon of flour, 20 wagons of guests and workmen and no less than 300 extra people who scrambled aboard for the ride. Running downhill, it reached speeds of up to 24 km (15 miles) per hour. But the primitive service only had one engine and frequently reverted to horse power. It wasn't until the *Rocket*, designed by his son Robert Stephenson and introduced in 1829, that steam engines became both successful and reliable.

Steam railways began to spring up across Britain and around the world. Stephenson and his son Robert were at the forefront of the new technology. They had at last dispelled the widely-held view that horses made a much better choice for transport than machines.

GEORGE STEPHENSON

HOW A STEAM LOCOMOTIVE WORKS

Each engine has a firebox. In it fuel is burned, usually coal although sometimes wood or oil. Next to the firebox is the boiler, full of water. After the firebox is lit, it heats the water and turns it into steam. The steam is heated in the sealed engine header tank until it reaches a high pressure, when it pushes its way through a valve to move a piston in a cylinder. It is the movement of the piston backwards and forwards which turns the wheels. A system of rods ensures that once the first wheel is turning, the rest of the wheels on the engine will go round as well.

The crew in the open cab consisted of a driver and a fireman. The fireman keeps the boiler stoked from the store of coal carried behind the cab so that there is always plenty of steam. He also makes sure there is enough water in the boiler. The driver moves the train by using the throttle, brake and reversing mechanism.

Both keep an eye out for trackside signals.

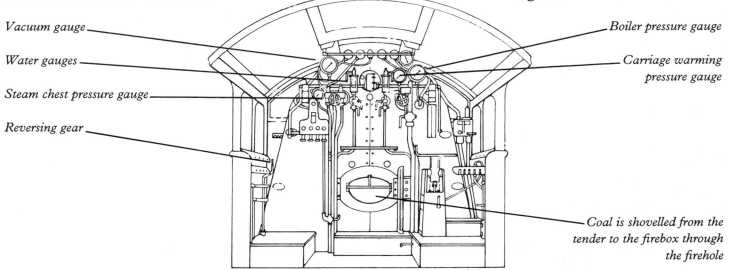

Vacuum gauge

Water gauges

Steam chest pressure gauge

Reversing gear

Boiler pressure gauge

Carriage warming pressure gauge

Coal is shovelled from the tender to the firebox through the firehole

FIREMAN'S SIDE

DRIVER'S SIDE

THE GOLDEN AGE

Within twenty years of there being rail services, trains were travelling at speeds of between 96 km (60 miles) per hour and 128 km (80 miles) per hour. Railways had a revolutionary effect. It is hard to believe how they changed the lives of people when nowadays air travel makes it possible for everyone to travel all over the globe. But railways were invented before even the first car was on the road.

Imagine what life would be like if you lived without cars, buses or trains, with only primitive cycles to transport you between places with a great deal of boneshaking. Roads were at best only bumpy tracks. Imagine the difference it made to people who had until then been forced to rely on the speed of a galloping horse.

Thanks to railways, people could travel long distances quite cheaply for the first time in their lives. Coal was inexpensive so the cost of tickets was low. For the first time, families began to live in different places. The ease with which they could return to visit encouraged sons and daughters to leave their farms and seek their fortune in cities and towns. Some went even further by steamship to America and then across to the other side of the continent by train. Reliable communication increased dramatically, too. When the railway system was established letters were carried more quickly than ever before.

The railways gave a tremendous boost to industry. Small businesses could expand their trade now that it was so economical to transport freight across the country. The price of goods fell and demand went up. It was an exciting time; railways represented the go-ahead spirit of the age.

Locomotives became the pride of the country. Drivers and firemen worked hard to keep them spotlessly clean and shining. The country was covered with a variety of railway companies, each with its brightly coloured, grand emblems. The locomotives were ornately painted in detail.

Not everyone was in favour of trains. There were thinkers of the day like poet William Wordsworth and writer John Ruskin who argued against the intrusion of railways into the countryside. They considered travelling by train no better than being packaged up and sent like a parcel.

The North Eastern Railway's coat of arms.

A third-class carriage, unprotected from the weather.

Railways were crucial to the United States when it was developing into a modern country. Trains helped to open up new frontiers, penetrating unknown territories on the giant continent, transporting settlers and their wares and linking small towns scattered over huge areas.

The arrival of the steam locomotive provided a huge boost to the North American economy. In the 1840s and 1850s numerous schools opened to educate railway engineers. They couldn't find enough men to satisfy the demand.

Every ambitious town fought for the best railway communications. Railway companies were powerful and rich – they demanded large cash payments from towns who wanted to be included on the line, otherwise they were bypassed and left in isolation while the rest of the country flourished. Salt Lake City, for example, was stranded nearly 100 miles from the first transcontinental route and had to battle to survive. The town of Plum Creek moved, lock, stock and barrel, half a mile to the west to be on the railway.

Pioneering railway companies included the Union Pacific, the Central Pacific, the Quincy, the Illinois Central and the Burlington Railroad, and all were vital to the life of the American states.

A first-class carriage used during the 18th century.

At first, the main aim of trains was to transport freight like coal, iron and, later, steel. But gradually the railway operators realised there was trade to be found among the population, now keen to travel from one town to the next on this speedy innovation. Soon a string of carriages were made to travel behind locomotives, varying from the luxurious to little more than a cart on tracks.

First-class carriages were built in the style of horse-drawn stagecoaches, richly decorated on the inside with curtains and polished wood finishes. The luggage was even loaded onto the roof, along with the guard, just as it was on stagecoaches. This habit of stowing the baggage on the roof stopped when it was realised that, with sparks flying out from the engine, it was a fire risk.

The second-class passengers travelled with a canopy over their heads but the sides were left open. The poorest people were put in third-class carriages and had to travel in open trucks, feeling not only the full force of the weather but also the grime of the locomotive, particularly smoky and unpleasant as the train passed through a tunnel. Sometimes holes were drilled in the floor to let the rainwater out before it became ankle deep. The earliest of the third-class carriages were called cauldron wagons, first used for coal and later for humans.

Sumptuous decoration and first-class service for those with the money to spend on luxurious travel.

All passengers, whatever price they paid for their ticket, had to climb down a stepladder to the ground. In those days stations didn't have a raised platform. As wide crinoline dresses were in fashion, it was particularly difficult for women.

In 1844 William Gladstone, a future British Prime Minister who was then President of the Board of Trade, helped to pass a new law called the 'Regulation of Railways Act'. It ordered that all the railway companies must provide covered carriages for third-class passengers at the set fare of one penny per mile. Even then greedy company bosses didn't want to splash out on comforts for its poorest customers. To comply with the law, they introduced carriages which were no more than boxes, with small slits providing the only ventilation and light. Often they ran these trains, called 'Parliamentary' services, only at night, to the maximum discomfort of the unfortunate passengers. Bare board seats for third-class travellers survived into the 1930s.

But thankfully conditions did improve as the golden age of steam wore on. It became fashionable for large families with sufficient wealth to hire a specially constructed saloon carriage for outings or holidays. Normally running on six wheels, the carriages had plenty of room for luggage and separate accommodation for servants.

Sleeping cars were introduced in the 1860s in America and came to Europe a decade later. Carriages were at first partitioned off by curtains. Later, two single beds were provided in a small compartment, one raised like a bunk, along with a sink and luggage rack.

Restaurant cars first made an appearance in 1879. However, travellers in the early days much preferred to cater for themselves.

Locomotives became bigger and faster, reaching the height of their popularity in the 1930s and 1940s. They were frequently described with numbers relating to their wheel arrangement. For example, a locomotive 4-6-4 has four leading wheels, six driving wheels and four trailing wheels.

TRACKS

George Stephenson not only developed locomotives but he also designed railway lines, following the principles used at the colliery railway where he had started work. This led to the railway width of 1.43 m (4 ft 8½ ins) being adopted across the world as standard track measurements.

Railway tracks were made from wooden sleepers which were laid on level ground with short distances between them. Two lengths of rails were put across them at right angles attached by chairs or baseplates screwed into the sleeper. Each length of rail was joined to the next by a fishplate. Beneath the rails and between the sleepers there was a pile of stone ballast. This was to improve drainage so rail lines did not get washed away in rainwater floods.

It was back-breaking work to lay rail lines and took huge numbers of men. There was little by way of equipment to help. Today the sleepers are made of concrete and the work is mostly done by machinery. Rails are bedded onto a rubber pad and held in place by strong steel springs. Instead of using fishplates, the rails are welded together, which gives the passengers in the moving trains a much smoother ride.

OVER AND UNDER

The invention of railways caused leaps forward in technology. Line builders soon became frustrated at being stopped in their tracks at rivers and hills or mountains.

With large supplies of cheap labour available, the first response to an obstacle of rock or cliff was to hack out a route using hand tools, like picks. It took huge amounts of effort from the labourers, known as navvies, to carve out a wide channel and it was slow going. Engineers began using dynamite, and advances in the effective use of explosives meant subsequent projects took half the time.

The first railway tunnel in the world for freight was an underground line at Newcastle Upon Tyne, built in 1770. The first railway tunnel to be used for passenger traffic was Tyler Hill Tunnel on the Canterbury and Whitstable Railway which opened on 4 May 1830 and measured 766 m (838 yards). Passengers used the route for more than 100 years. A tunnel more than double its length was then opened in 1832; called the Glenfield tunnel, it was on the Leicester and Swannington Railway.

Distinguished engineers of the era, like Marc Brunel, turned their attention to digging tunnels beneath river beds. It was he who designed and built the Thames Tunnel, which was started in 1825 and finally opened to pedestrian traffic on 25 March 1843. The parallel bores were adapted for use by the East London Railway under engineer Sir John Hawkshaw and steam train passengers were travelling under the Thames by the end of 1869.

It was Sir John Hawkshaw who built Britain's longest railway tunnel, the one that goes under the River Severn to link England and South Wales. It took 14 years to construct and was opened on 1 September 1886. Although it measures more than 7 km ($4^{1}/_{2}$ miles), only about a quarter of it is underwater.

America's longest underwater tunnel is the Bay Area Rapid Transit, known as BART, which links Oakland to San Francisco. It is 5.5 kms ($3^{1}/_{2}$ miles) long and opened in 1974.

The shortest tunnel in the States is the Bee Rock Tunnel near Appalachia, Virginia. Opened in 1891, it is just 9 m (10 yards) long.

Also, engineers built bridges to overcome hazards in their path. The world's first iron bridge was on the Stockton and Darlington Railway over the River Gaunless at West Auckland. Built in 1825, it was replaced in 1901 and the original re-erected as a museum piece.

Probably the best known bridge-builder of the age was Isambard Kingdom Brunel who worked extensively on Britain's railway network.

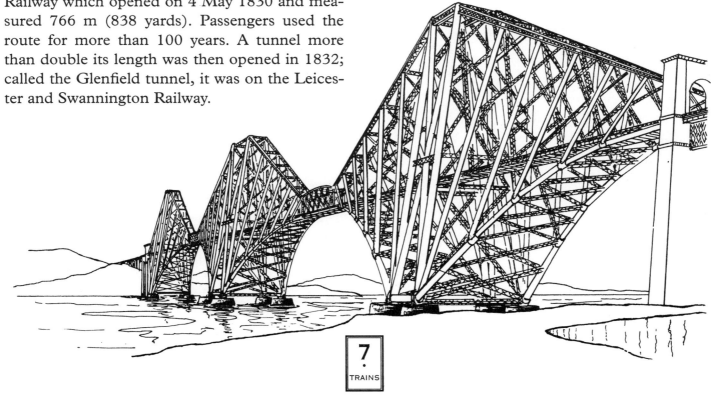

THE STEAM LOCOMOTIVE

WHEELS See Diagram 1

Score, cut out and fold parts **1**. Curl rim around wheel, glue edge of rim to it and tuck the end inside. Hold until dry.

Cut out square centre of **2** before cutting out wheel shape.

Score folds in **3** before cutting slots to separate end tabs.

Now cut out **3** and fold into square tube shape, tucking and gluing edge tab inside. Hold until dry.

Push **3** (axle) through square hole in **2** and fold back tabs on white side of **2** and glue down.

Glue rim of **1** to the white side of **2**, keeping **1** central on **2** to make a good shape.

Make up all large wheels and axles **1**, **2** and **3** plus all small wheels and axles, **4**, **5** & **10** and **6**, **7**, & **10** in the same way. (Spare axles are provided).

Cut out and glue **11** & **12**, **13** & **14** and **15** & **16** together, but do not glue to ends of axles yet. Make sure all crescent-shaped counterweights on large wheels line up on both sides of wheels.

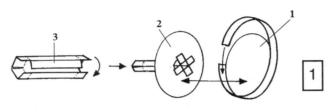

CHASSIS See Diagram 2

Score all folds on parts **19**, **20** & **21**, and cut out all holes marked with a dot.

Cut out parts **19**, **20** & **21** and fold all tabs on **20** & **21**, gluing end tabs **1** & **2** on part **20** into position on **21** to form rectangular ring shape.

Score, cut out and fold spacers **22**, **23**, **24** & **25**, and glue tabs **3**, **4**, **5**, & **6** into positions inside chassis **20** & **21**.

When glue is dry, bend and fold **19** to fit over chassis **20** & **21**. Ensure that all curves are followed as closely as possible, with the ends folded down at right angles. The red end should be at the front.

Once shaped correctly, glue **19** to **20** & **21**, using guidelines under **19** to help positioning.

Push large wheels and axles **1**, **2** & **3** through holes **7**, **8** & **9**, and small wheel and axle **6**, **7**, & **10** through hole **10** in chassis. Fix corresponding wheels to other end of axles. Ensure counterweights are lined up, but do not glue wheels to chassis or

they will not rotate.

Score, cut out and fold spacer **26**, gluing tabs in position under middle chassis, taking care not to obstruct main axles.

Very carefully cut out **27** & **28**, and glue along corresponding edges of **19**, so that small lip hangs down.

Score, cut out and fold parts **29** and glue into small tubes. Cut out discs **30** and glue to ends of **29**, then glue **29** into positions **11** & **12** on front of footplate.

Score and cut out parts **31**, folding tabs down and bending to fit over front splasher tabs **13**. Glue tabs inside **13** and pull down to form wheel-arch. Repeat for parts **32** and tabs **14** and parts **33**, trailing the wheel-arch over the curve of the footplate.

Cut and fold nameplates **34**, gluing tabs to top of centre arches **32** facing outwards.

Score, cut out and fold **35**, gluing over white lines on front of **19**.

Cut out **36** & **37** and glue along white lines in front of **35**.

FRONT AND REAR BOGIES See Diagrams 3 & 4

Score, cut out and fold **38**, gluing tabs **15** in place to form box. Hold until dry.

Score, cut and fold **39**, **40**, **41** & **42**. Form and glue **39** into small tube and push through hole in **38** by tab **16**. Splay out end tabs on white side of **38** and glue cross to disc **40**, but not to **38**.

Glue ends of **42** to **38** over disc, allowing disc to rotate between **38** and **42**. Push spindle through hole in **41** from black side, splay tabs and glue to white side of **41**. Glue tab **16** in position on **38**. Pass small wheels and axles **4** & **5**

through holes in front of bogie **38**, gluing on remaining wheels **13** & **14** as before. Take completed bogie and glue tabs **17** and part **41** up inside front of chassis, ensuring wheels are aligned with arches. Bogie assembly should swivel about spindle **39** and bogie wheels should sit level on ground with other wheels.

Score, cut out and fold **43** & **44**, then cut out **45** & **46** and glue in place on **43** & **44**. Glue tabs **18** & **19** to rear of chassis, covering rear bogie wheels. Ensure parts are all square.

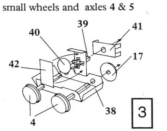

PISTON & VALVE ASSEMBLY See Diagram 5 & 6

Score, cut out and fold parts 47 & 48, including dot heads. Fold tops down and glue tabs 20 to sides. Fold in all other tabs then roll-up and glue tail piece around sides to form a box, ensuring fit is good and clean. Hold until dry.

Cut out and roll parts 49 & 50 with grey area to one end of tube. Roll until small enough to fit into hole in valve gear. Push tube in black end first. Grey end should protrude and be left unglued. Cut out 51 & 52 and glue to other end

of 47 & 48. Score, cut and fold parts 53, 54, 55 & 56 and glue to each end of 47 & 48 in line with front valley fold line. Glue completed valve gear up underneath footplate 19 either side of the front bogies. Very carefully cut out coupling parts 57 and 58, removing the dotted sections and folding tabs 21. Glue 57 & 58 to underside of footplate, taking care to line up wheel centres with coupling motion. Piston at front of coupling should slide into valve gear tube. If coupled wheels are not required to turn, a spot of glue on the four driving wheels will hold the couplings 57 & 58 more securely. Ensure that crescent counterweights on wheels are all lined up at top of wheels.

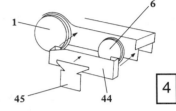

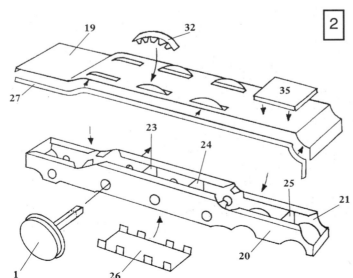

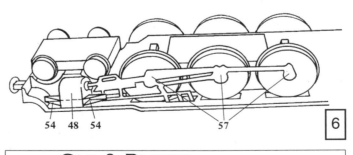

CAB & BARREL See Diagram 7 & 8

Score, cut out and fold **59**. Glue into square ring shape. When dry, glue to **35**, following white lines. Cut out **60** and fold down end discs. Roll main section to form tube, with discs at either end. Cut out strip **61** and glue side **22** along line **22** inside tube. Hold until dry. Glue side **23** to corresponding position in tube and hold in place with elastic bands and spring-

clips until dry.

Remove clips and glue discs into ends to form good tube shape. Cut out **62** and roll into conical tube shape. Cut out strip **63** and glue to edges of **62**. When dry, slide small end of **62** over green end of **60** to first black line and carefully glue in place. Cut out and roll **64**, gluing strip **65** as before. Score and cut out **66**, folding tabs back to fit into disc large end of **64**. Glue in place

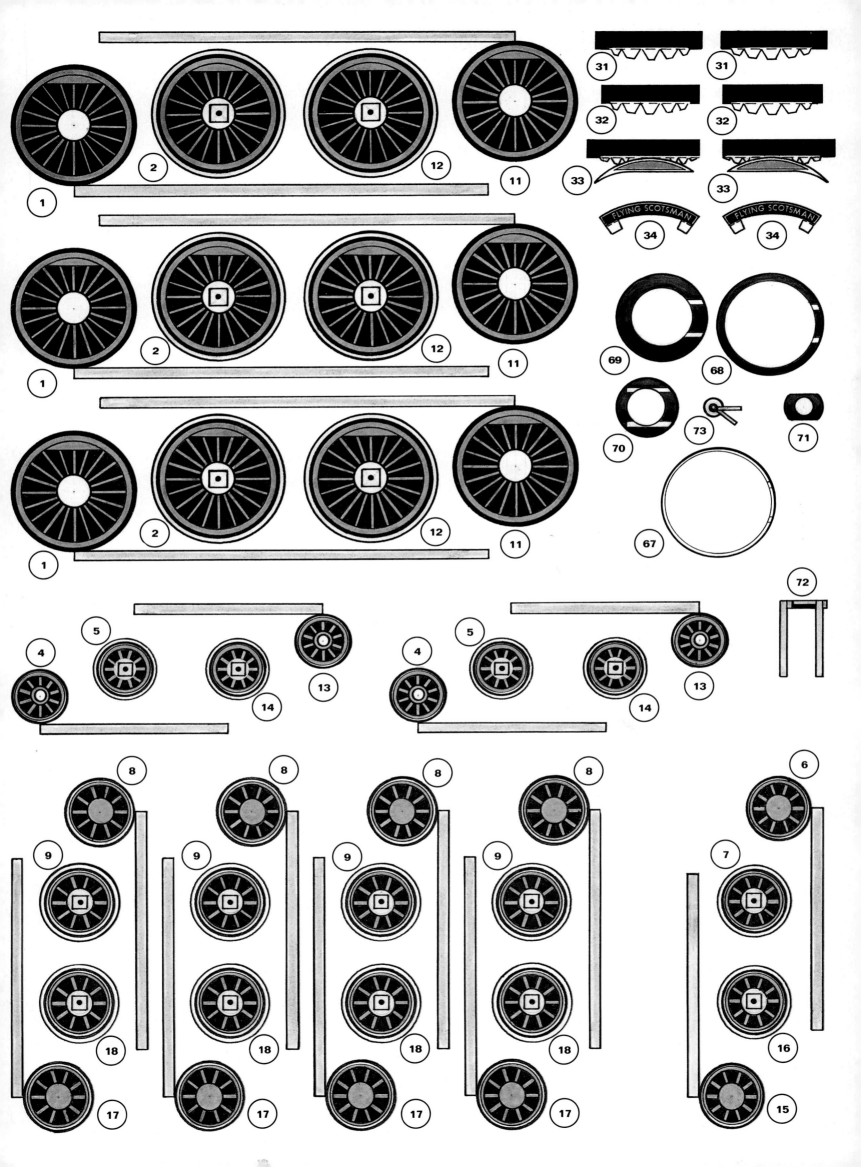

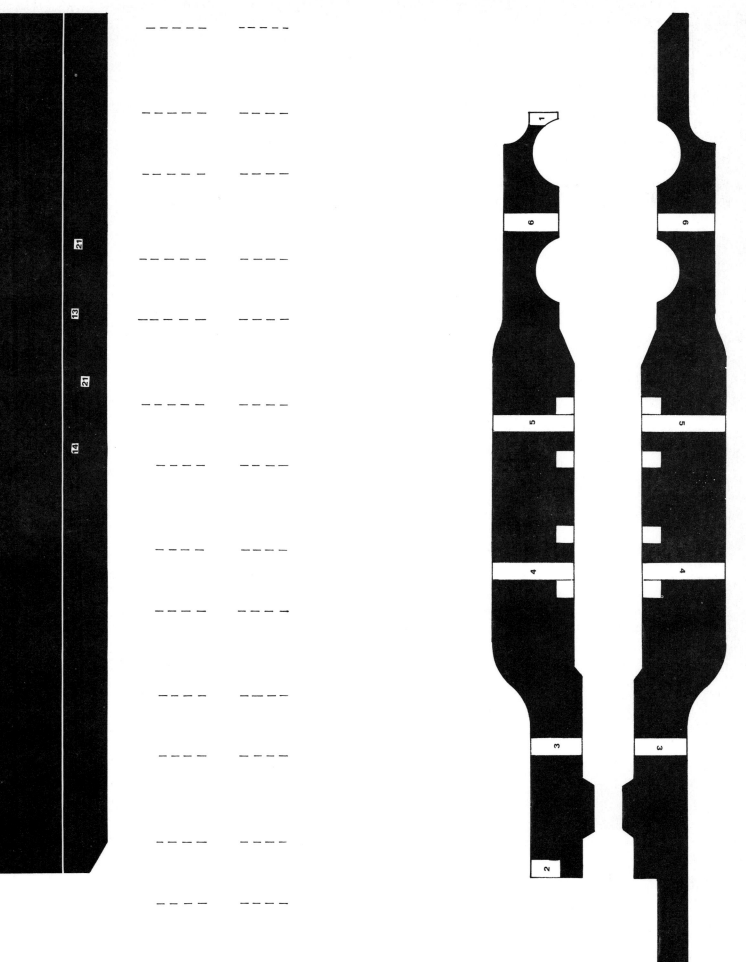

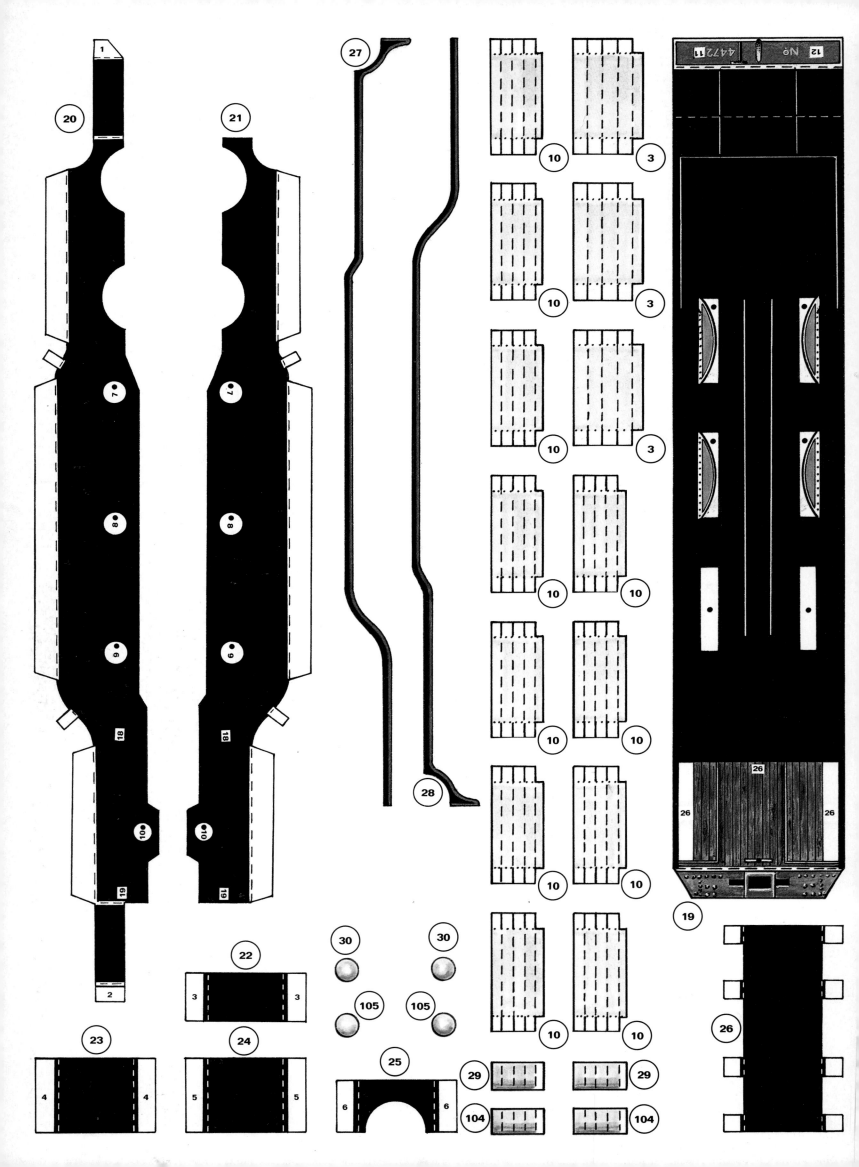

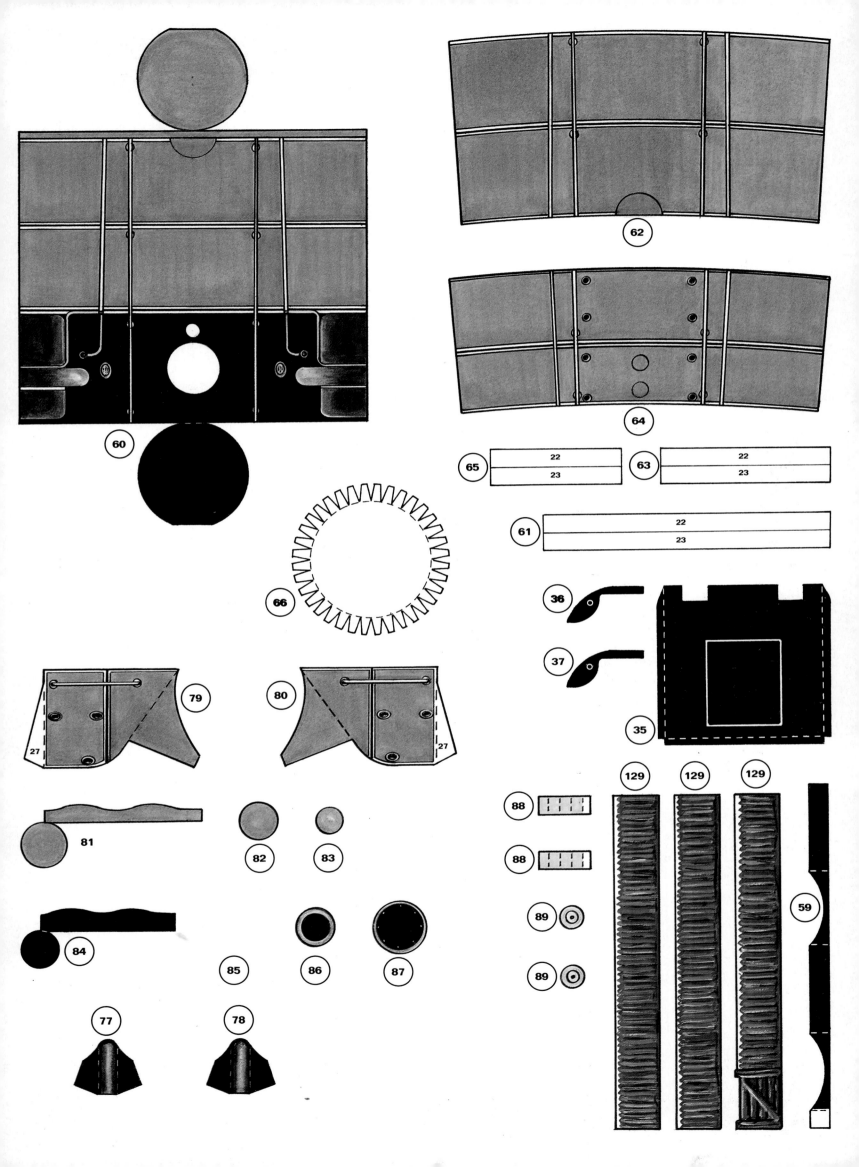

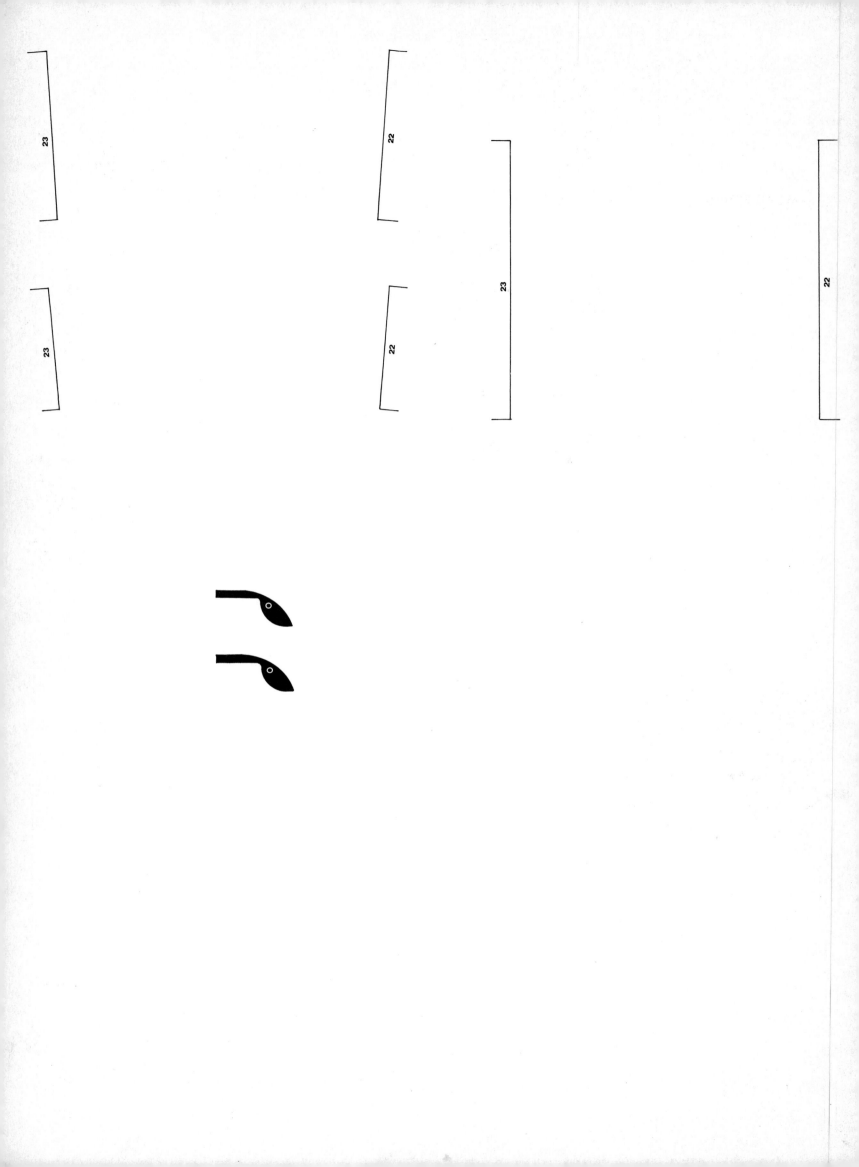

23

23

22

22

23

22

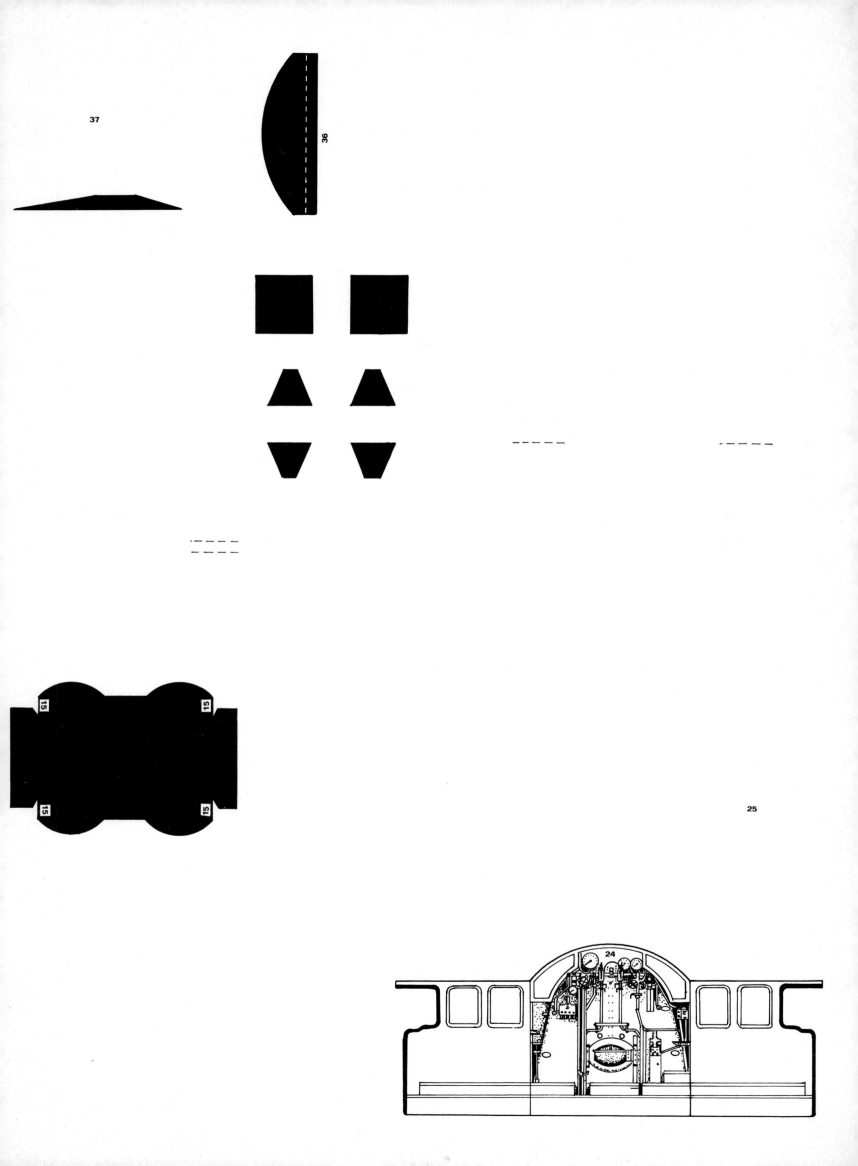

37

36

15 15

15 15

25

24

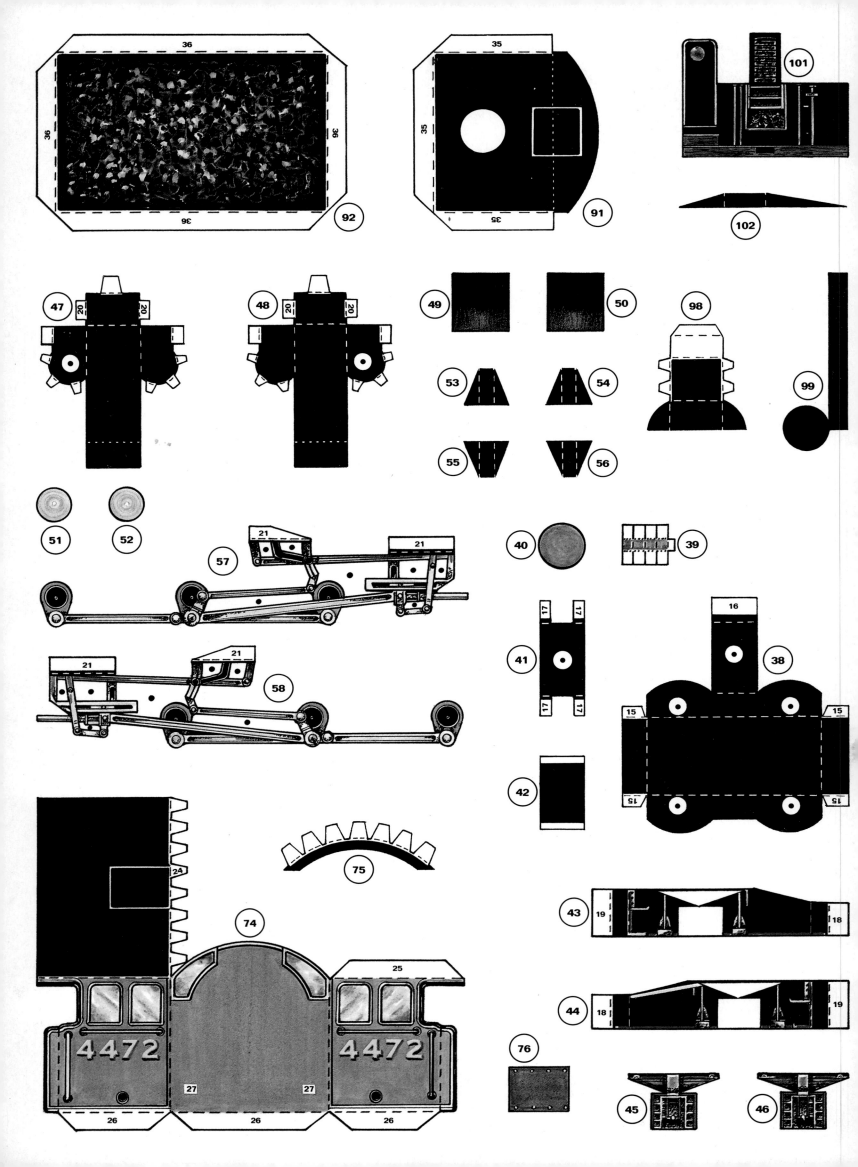

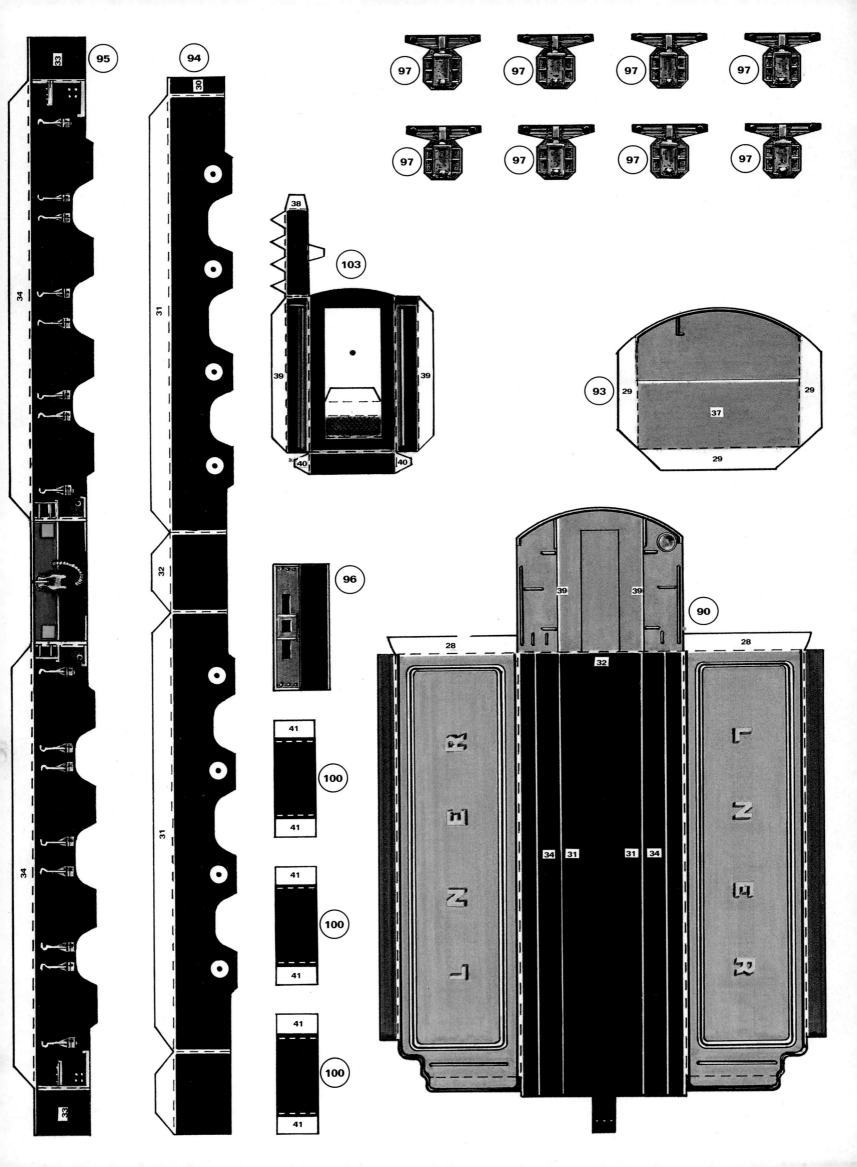

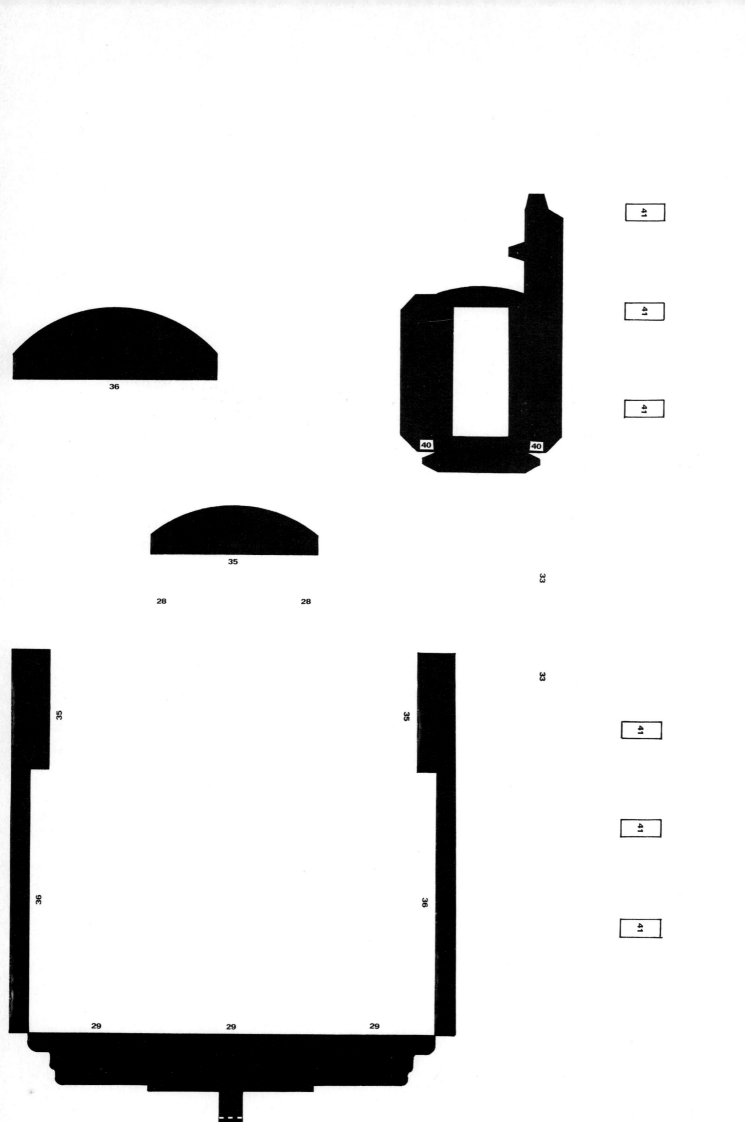

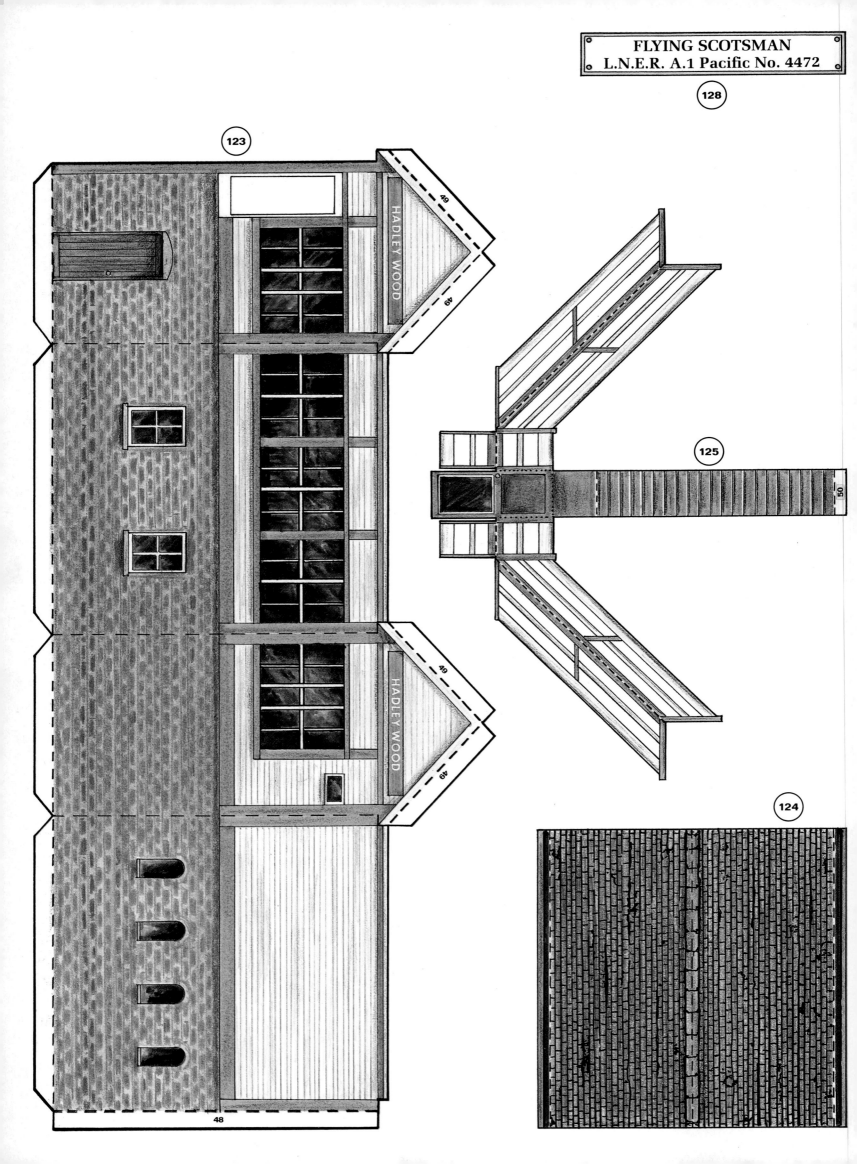

FLYING SCOTSMAN
L.N.E.R. A.1 Pacific No. 4472

with tabs protruding. Carefully glue wide end of **62** onto tabs of **66**, making cleanest joint possible, ensuring graphics on barrel line up. Cut out parts **67, 68, 69, 70 & 71**, gluing them together in a pile with **67** at the bottom and **71** placed centrally on top. Make sure the two white lines are lined up on all pieces. Cut out **72** and glue along white lines across front of dome. Cut out **73** and glue to **71** on top of dome. Glue completed dome to black front disc of barrel. Score, cut out and fold cab **74**, curling roof down and round to follow curve of roofline. Glue tabs **24** to control bulkhead and side tab **25** to edge of roof. Score cut and fold **75** and use to pull back of roof into shape. Glue up inside roof along marked line. Glue tabs **26** into position on footplate **19**, lining up back edge of cabin sides with rear edge of footplate. Cut out and glue **76** to roof of **74** following white lines. Once cab is dry, line up and glue barrel to

superstructure **59** and cabin bulkhead **74**. Ensure barrel is level and straight.
Score, cut and fold parts **77 & 78**, gluing into positions between superstructure and barrel, above valve gear. Score, cut out and fold parts **79 & 80**, gluing tabs **27** to front of **74** whilst gluing other edges to barrel and footplate. Cut out dome parts **81, 82 & 83**, folding **81** and rolling rim under top as with wheels. Glue into position before gluing **82** then **83** onto top of **81** to form dome. Glue into mid-position on top of barrel, trimming off excess rim to ensure good fit. Follow the same procedure for assembling funnel **84, 85 & 86**. Before gluing funnel to barrel; cut out, curve and glue **87** onto white disc at front of barrel. Then glue **84** to **87**. Score, cut out and fold parts **88**, gluing into small tubes. Cut out and glue parts **89** to one end of **88**, and glue finished pieces onto barrel just in front of cab.

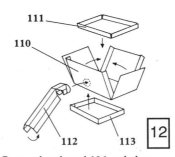

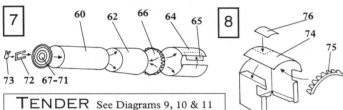

TENDER See Diagrams 9, 10 & 11

Score and cut out **90**, folding up into box and gluing tabs **28** in place. Fold top edges in to about 45°. Score, cut and fold **91**, gluing tabs **35** in place towards the rear of the tender, following guidelines shown.
Score, cut and fold coal **92** and glue tabs **36** in position in top of tender, butt up to **91**, using guidelines. Score, cut out and fold bulkhead **93**, gluing tabs **29** in place to form front of tender. Score, cut out and fold **94**, gluing tab **30** in place, ensuring dotted holes are removed first. Glue tabs **31 & 32** to underside of tender **90**, following inner guidelines, with tab **32** at the rear of tender. Score, cut and fold spacers **100**, gluing tabs **41** in position on **94** as with engine chassis. Take remaining four sets of wheels and axles **8, 9 & 10** and assemble as before. Push axles through holes in **94** before attaching wheels **17 & 18**. Score, cut out and fold **95** the same as **94**. Cut out **96** and

glue face-out to tabs **33**, forming ring shape. Glue tabs **34** in place on base of tender **90**, around wheel assembly. Ensure all is square and that wheels move freely. Cut out parts **97** and glue in position on **95** over wheels, as on rear bogies of engine. Score, cut out and fold **98 & 99**, gluing **98** into box form and **99** into funnel shape. Glue both pieces in position on **91** using white guidelines. Cut out **101** and glue to front of **93** position **37**. Score, cut out and fold **102** into 'U' shape and glue onto **101** and **93**. Score, cut out and fold **103** ensuring removal of dotted section.
Pull tab **38** down around top edge like cab roof, and glue in place. Glue tabs **40** into place to form doorway.
When complete, glue tabs **39** into place on rear of tender, with tops of **103 & 90** level. Score, cut out and fold buffers **104 & 105** as before and glue in position on rear of tender.

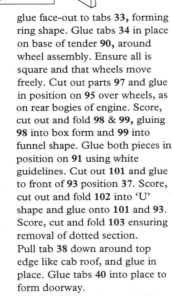

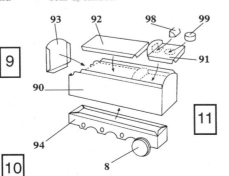

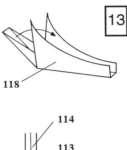

Cut out baseboard **106** and glue to slightly larger piece of thick card. Trim excess card. Cut out parts **107 & 108**, gluing white sides of **107** to white sides of **108**. Glue one edge of each part to lines on base **106** where rails should go, to form rail supports. Cut out parts **109** and glue to top of **107 & 108**, forming T-shaped rails. Take care that they are straight and level. Score, cut out and fold **110** and glue tabs **42** in position to form box. Score, cut and fold **111** and glue into top of **110** with water

level about 5mm below top of tank. Score, cut out and fold **112** to form angled tube. Glue together, then glue disc **43** in position on tank. Score, cut out and fold **113** and glue into ring shape. Glue edge of **113** to base of **110**, keeping central. Score, cut out and fold **114 & 115** into square-shaped legs. Glue **114** up inside ring **113** in front corners of tank **110**, with tabs exposed for gluing to baseboard. Glue parts **115** in remaining corners, to rear of tank with the three tabs away from back edge. Splay all tabs and glue to the left side of base **106** using guide squares. Score, cut out and fold **116**, ensuring small dotted holes are made. Glue into tube, folding top into pyramid shape. Cut out and fold **117**, removing dotted parts, and gluing tube together as before. Fold tube up at right-angles to base along white dashes. Score, cut out and fold **118**, gluing tabs **44** in position, before gluing tabs **45** in position on **116** to form signal support. When dry, glue base of **117** to tab **46** with signal post upright. Cut out parts **119, 120 & 121**, then take three matchsticks and cut into 15mm

BASEBOARD, WATERTANK, SIGNAL BOX & SIGNALS
See Diagrams 12, 13, 14, 15 & 16

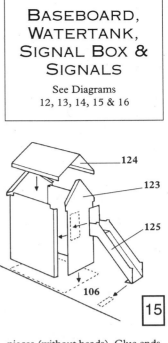

pieces (without heads). Glue ends of matchsticks to back of large circles on **119, 120 & 121**. When dry, push matchsticks through holes in signal posts, with red signals on small post **117** and top of **116** and yellow signal in lower holes on **116**.
Glue **116** on right-hand side of base **106** over white square, with signals facing left and **118** overhanging track. Hold until dry, and make sure signals move slowly. Score, cut out and fold **122** into box shape, gluing tabs to complete box. Glue tab **47** in position near base of **116**. Score, cut out and fold **123**, gluing tab **48** in position. Glue building **123** down onto base **106** with windows facing forwards. Score and cut out **124**, folding to fit roof line of **123**. Glue roof to tabs of **49**. Score, cut out and fold **125**, with stairs dropping down at 45° angle. Fold handrails in half and glue together with colour both sides, before folding handrails inwards and gluing to edge of stairs. When dry, glue door in position on end of **123** and tab **50** onto base **106**. Score, cut out and fold figures **126 & 127** and glue to model wherever desired. If care is taken borders can be cut from figures. Cut out nameplate **128** and glue near front of base **106**. Finally cut out fencing **129** and glue to rear edge of base **106**, with gate-piece to right of signal box.

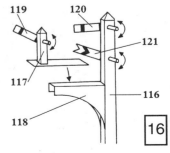

IF IN DOUBT –
CONSULT PHOTOGRAPH ON BACK COVER OF THIS BOOK
GOOD LUCK!

A different style of bridge building which became popular was the *cantilever* bridge. Perhaps the best known of all railway bridges has this design – the Forth Bridge in Scotland. Designed by John Fowler and Benjamin Baker, the Forth Bridge was opened on 4 March 1890 after eight years' work at a cost of £3,000,000. The builder was William Arrol.

It has three cantilever towers rising 103 m (340 ft) out of the water, which support two main spans measuring 520 m (1,710 ft) each. In total, the bridge is 2,522 m (8,298 ft) long. During construction, the bridge consumed 54,000 tons of steel and needed 6,500,000 rivets to hold it all in place. Fifty seven workers died while building work was in process.

It has also needed constant painting. The bridge took a band of 29 men about three years to apply 56 tons of paint to its steelwork. By the time they had finished it was time to start all over again. Nowadays just four painters using spray machines keep its paintwork fresh.

The world's highest railway bridge goes across the Mala Rijeka Gorge in former Yugoslavia. At 198 m (650 ft) above the ground, five steel spans bedded into concrete piers carry the trains.

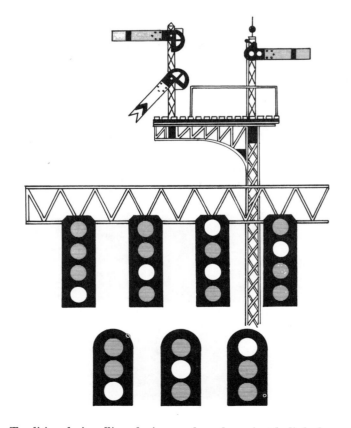

Traditional signalling devices and modern signals linked to a central computer system.

SIGNALS

When trains were first brought into commercial use, the network relied on hand signals to guide the drivers. The guard or a railway policeman waved flags and batons indicating to drivers whether the line ahead was clear. Points were also changed by hand, a job done by train drivers.

As the speed of trains increased, semaphore signals on posts were put up on the tracksides to give drivers advanced signals.

In the 1850s a mechanical semaphore system was invented. A signalman could then send a code down the rail line which put the appropriate signal in the correct position. The signalman was housed in a box by the railway line where he faced an array of waist-high handles which controlled the signals across an area. The box was raised to accommodate the machinery he operated, and it also gave him a good view of all the oncoming train traffic.

The signal itself was made of wood, sometimes with a metal band for extra strength. It measured about 25 cm (10 in) and was painted red and white. Although there were variations, in general terms a horizontal signal, lit at night by a red light, meant stop. When the arm pointed downwards and carried a green light in darkness, it was clear to proceed.

Each railway company had refined details in their signalling which avid enthusiasts have memorised down the years. And each company went on to develop its own set of signals for shunting and sidings work.

The signalman also had a selection of other equipment designed to tell him at the push of a button whether the line out of his sight was clear or blocked. Another device to prevent crashes on single lines was an electric key token instrument. A driver only received a clear signal after he had been handed a metal rod with an appropriate code. It meant two trains should never have been on the same track at the same time.

Electronic switchboards covering vast areas have replaced these signal boxes. Now the signalman can signal directly to the drivers' cab as well as sparking track-side lights. In the interests of safety, a signalman can even halt the train himself if he has to without needing help from the driver.

SOME STEAM TRAIN RECORDS

The first steam trip reaching 160 km (100 miles) per hour was made by the Empire State Express in 1893 on the New York Central and Hudson River Railroad.

The fastest ever steam train was a streamlined locomotive called *Mallard* which travelled at 203 km (126 miles) per hour down a slope in July 1938. It was dashing between London and Edinburgh and among its coaches was a special speed recording car which verified the record.

The man behind *Mallard* was British engineer Sir Nigel Gresley, and it was built by the London North Eastern Railway at Doncaster in the same year it set the unbeaten record.

The world record for the fastest ever run between two stations is held in America by the 1935 Hiawatha service, spanning 665 km (412 miles) between Chicago and Minneapolis. It averaged 128 km (80 miles) per hour over a 127 km (78.9 mile) stretch of track.

The last steam locomotive built for British Rail was the *Evening Star* in 1960. It worked pulling freight and passenger services until 1966 when it was withdrawn.

The world's longest rail bridge runs for nearly 7 km (4¹/₂ miles) in Metairie, Louisiana, USA. Called the Huey P. Long bridge, it was opened for its locomotive traffic back in 1935.

The first transcontinental railway linked up on 10 May 1869 at Promontory in Utah, USA. It had been constructed in two spurs, one from the east, the other from the west, and took six years to complete.

The Liverpool and Manchester Railway which opened in 1830 was the first to rely entirely upon steam engines.

The first train-ferry operating between Dover, England and Dunkerque, France, came into service in 1936. It transported the carriages of the train which were off-loaded to continue their journey from London to Paris or Brussels.

10 ITEMS NEEDED BY A GUARD ON A STEAM TRAIN STATION

A whistle.
A braided cap with badge in the livery of the company he worked for.
A wheeled water carrier to replenish supplies in the dining car.
A handbell to announce the arrival of a train.
A clipper to punch the tickets, proving it had been inspected
(the first card tickets were made in 1837).
A fob or pocket watch.
A carriage key to secure unused carriages.
A flag to signal stop or go to the driver.
An oil lamp used at night for signalling the driver.
A broad-based oil can to fill up lamps.

MODERN TRAINS

UNDERGROUND

When streets became choked up, transport planners decided to go underground. The first railway under the streets was built in 1863 to connect the mainline station of Paddington, London, to the commercial centre of Farringdon Street. But the line bore little resemblance to the sophisticated maze of tunnels deep under the city which was to spring up in the early 20th century. Railway builders simply dug a trench and covered it to make a tunnel. As the carriages were pulled by small steam locomotives, filth and fumes were pumped out into the confined tunnel with poor ventilation which made for an unpleasant journey. The steam condensers designed to combat the problem were barely effective. Stations as well as tunnels became shrouded in smoke.

Despite the problems, the advantages of taking traffic from the streets and putting it underground were apparent. By 1890, the first electric underground railway had opened, connecting the City of London with suburbs south of the Thames. Its tunnel went beneath the river bed. France introduced the Metro under the streets of Paris in 1900, and America launched its underground railway in New York in 1904.

Moscow didn't open a system until 1933 but made up for its lateness by the grandeur of its stations, which attracted fame worldwide.

London still has the most expansive underground system in the world. It can boast 409 route km (254 miles) underground, sometimes as deep as 67 m (220 ft) below the pavements. At peak times one line can carry as many as 50,000 people an hour.

Some underground trains are fully automated and don't need a driver. The Post Office began using driverless trains to carry mailbags underground as long ago as 1927. In the future it is likely many underground systems will operate without staff, at the flick of a computer switch.

DIESEL

Diesel engines were pioneered by Rudolph Diesel, a German born in Paris. His first successful model was launched in 1897. It relied on oil instead of coal or petrol. Its disadvantage was the time it took to get up speed. Nevertheless, diesels went into production in Germany in 1912 and were soon used throughout Europe. Later, diesel engines were often used in conjunction with an electric generator to gain a higher speed.

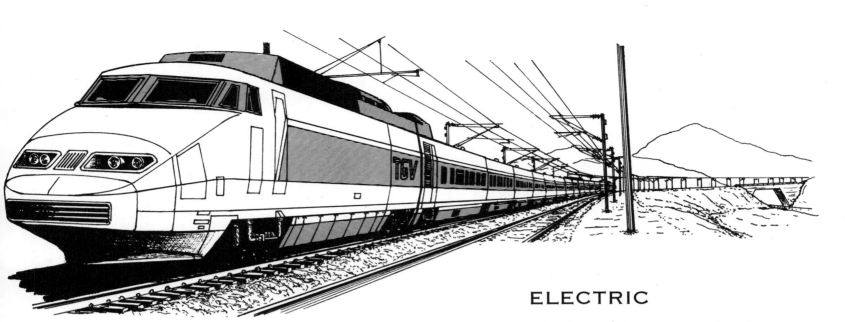

ELECTRIC

Faster than diesel, cleaner than steam, electric trains are the most successful ancestor of Stephenson's *Rocket*. Electric trains were developed more than 100 years ago. The first ever ran in Northern Ireland between Portrush and Giant's Causeway in 1883. They don't need to carry fuel but rely on cables or rails to generate power. Their biggest drawback is the cost of building the lines they require. The fastest train in the world is electric. The TGV, which stands for *Train à Grande Vitesse* (or high speed train), was introduced in France in 1983. It needs its own special track to achieve its best performance. In 1990 the record was set on the Paris to Lyon route of a breathtaking 515 km (320 miles) per hour.

FREIGHT

Most cargo now travels by road in hefty juggernauts or by air. Even much of the post is sent via motorways to our doors now. The downfall of

freight trains came because it took so long for consignments to work their way through marshalling yards. Computers have helped slash the waiting time. Also, few railways run directly to the destination needed by customers, with only 182 stations nationwide handling freight. They must pick up the goods from the nearest station and manage delivery for the last few miles themselves.

MOUNTAIN

Stephenson would have been overjoyed to see a railway climbing a steep hill. He believed it would be impossible but, thanks to rack and cable systems, railways have spread to even the most remote and inaccessible places.

The oldest European rack railway is in Switzerland, dating from 1872, and it scales a one-in-three slope. A rack track looks like a ladder, and works with cogs, giving the train something to grip.

For the most hostile terrain, funicular or cable cars are the answer. The downward moving carriage pulls the upward one to its destination. These cars can be weighted with water or run by electricity.

MONORAILS

Like underground trains, monorails suspended above the ground have the advantage of bypassing traffic congestion. These trains either run on a single rail or are suspended from wheels locked to the overhead rails. Monorails have been used in Germany since 1901 when one called the Schwehebahn was constructed to connect towns divided by a rocky river valley. Now they are often seen in amusement parks. Trippers can get a bird's eye view of the attractions on offer in a rewarding and fun way.

Unlucky David Brook was the first fatality on British railways, on 5 December 1821. He was walking home along the Middleton Railway in a storm and failed to see or hear an early steam engine which was pulling a string of coal wagons.

The most notable early victim, however, was Liverpool MP William Huskisson, who was run down by Stephenson's *Rocket* on its first day in operation on the Liverpool and Manchester line. In a bid to save his life, Stephenson himself leapt to the control of another engine, *Northumbrian*, to take the stricken man to a surgeon. Despite establishing a world speed record of 58 km (36 miles) per hour on the journey, his dash was in vain and Mr Huskisson died.

Author Charles Dickens was involved in a crash at Staplehurst, Kent, on 9 June 1865, after the train he was on was derailed on a viaduct. Ten other passengers were killed outright. It is said Dickens never recovered from the shock and he died exactly five years later.

Britain's worst rail disaster happened at Quintinshill, north of Carlisle, in 1915. Two trains collided and a third ploughed into the wreckage, killing 227 people. The most catastrophic crash ever happened in France in 1917 when a packed troop train went out of control, claiming 543 lives.

But although there have been smashes and crashes, railway operators have learned by their mistakes. For example, a system of locking compartment doors in France was ended in 1842 when 48 people died in a coach pile-up. And signalling has been refined and improved after causing a variety of bumps and scrapes.

For years it has been compulsory for all train accidents to be reported to the Ministry of Transport. So it has been easy to keep a tally of the number of train crashes in Britain. And figures prove it is far safer to travel by rail than by coach, car or motorbike.

The main risk to users is not from the trains themselves but from obstacles put in their path by vandals, which can cause major derailments.

10 GREAT TRAIN STORIES

Thomas the Tank Engine – by Rev. W. Awdry, made into a popular cartoon series, with the voice of Ringo Starr as Thomas.

Murder on the Orient Express – by Agatha Christie. Filmed in Hollywood, full of famous stars playing the characters from the book.

Brief Encounter – written by Noel Coward and made into an internationally successful film starring Trevor Howard and Celia Johnson.

The Railway Children – written by E. Nesbit and filmed with Jenny Agutter, Bernard Cribbins and Sally Thomsett in the starring roles.

The Titfield Thunderbolt – 'Ealing comedy' written by T.E.B. Clarke and starring Stanley Holloway.

The Lady Vanishes – a film of the book *The Wheel Spins* written by Ethel Lina White. Filmed twice.

The General – comedy film made in 1926 directed by and starring Buster Keaton.

Oh! Mr Porter – a 1937 comedy film starring Will Hay.

The Ghost Train – comedy from a play by Arnold Ridley, filmed twice.

The Taking of Pelham 123 – film about gunmen who hold up a subway train in New York, from the book by John Godey.

◎ GREAT RAILWAY JOURNEYS ◎

The Orient Express, travelling from Paris to Istanbul, the gateway to Asia, was launched in the heyday of rail travel and still runs today. It is now famed for the old-fashioned luxury of its carriages and the splendour of its menu.

The Trans-Siberian Express runs on an astonishing 9,332 km (5,786 mile) line bridging Europe and Asia. It took eight years to construct most of the line in the snowy wastes of what was then Czarist Russia. Even then passengers had to face a ferry trip across one lake. It wasn't until 1916 that a track was built alongside the rocky shore of Lake Baikal. Nowadays, it takes nine days to do the journey which once would have taken travellers on horseback as long as two years. The first cinema ever to be run on a train was installed on the Trans-Siberian line by a French company in 1913 when travellers could watch the latest silent black and white movie at a cost of 50 kopeks or one shilling.

The Canadian Pacific Railway runs across the North American continent, a trip of thousands of miles. Although planned in 1871, it wasn't finally completed until 1885.

Luxury trains were first introduced on the 1,542 km (956 mile) route between Cape Town and Pretoria in South Africa in 1903. *The Blue Train* was introduced in 1939 and is now thought to be the plushest service in the world.

Through trains between Sydney and Perth in Australia were not in use until 1970. The 3,970 km (2,461 mile) route includes the world's longest length of straight track, measuring almost 483 km (300 miles), and takes three days.

In Peru, the world's highest standard gauge railway operates among the snowy peaks of the Andes mountains, on the Morococha Branch at La Cim, an amazing 4,803 m (15,800 ft) above sea level. The train travels at a height greater than Mt Blanc, the biggest mountain in Europe.

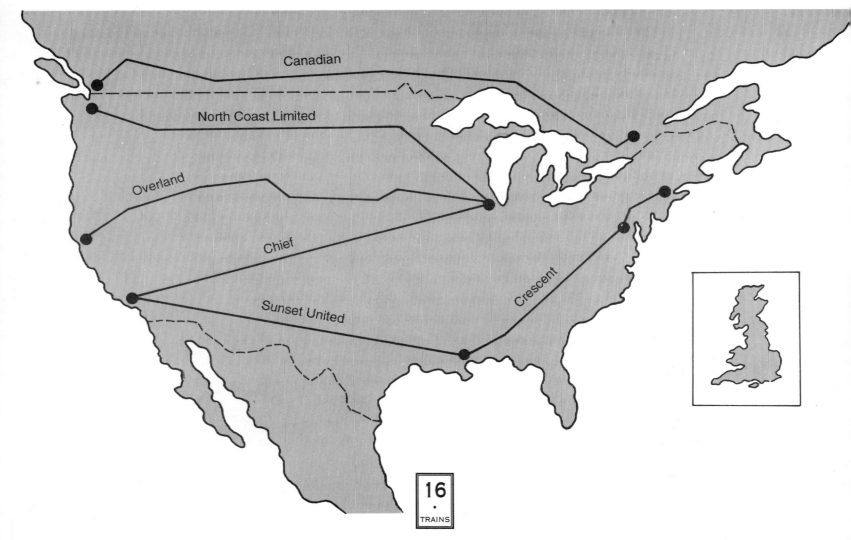

First published in Great Britain in 1994 by Parragon Book Service Ltd 4 Mulberry Close, Rosslyn Hill, Hampstead, London, NW3 5UP.
© Parragon Book Service Ltd 1994 ISBN 1 85813 448 X. Typeset by the R&B Partnership. Printed in Great Britain. Reprinted 1994.